Scissor Skills Patterns
with a Purpose

Author .... Linda Milliken
Illustrations .... Barb Lorseyedi
Cover Illustration...................... Brenda Sexton

EP009 • © Highsmith® Inc. 1992, 2008
W5527 State Road 106, P.O. Box 800
Fort Atkinson, WI 53538
www.edupressinc.com

Table of Contents

Before You Begin

Check all hand positions before any cutting takes place. Here are some things to look for: splayed fingers; cutting with "thumbs-down"; cutting with two hands; holding the scissors on the joints; failing to rotate the paper with cutting; and keeping the hand and the paper resting against the table throughout the cutting. You can help correct these bad habits by showing children the correct way to hold a pair of scissors—using the fingertips of the thumb and first two fingers to control the scissors.

Give children basic instructions before you begin cutting projects. Demonstrate how to cut out separate shapes if there are more than one on the paper. Show them how to hold the paper and rotate it as they cut. With the continued practice in this book you will see an improvement in fine motor control.

Using the Book

Skills Checklist (page 4)

- Use as a tool for tracking and assessing fine motor development.
- Use as a planning guide for aides or volunteers working with children who need specific skill and motor coordination practice.
- Refer to individual progress for report card preparation and parent conferences.

Practice Pages (pages 5–11)

- Reproduce pages for skill practice prior to beginning a project.
- Conserve paper by printing on the back of unused school newsletters, worksheets, and other paper extras that would otherwise be thrown away.
- Encourage children to color practice pages before cutting. Not only will they develop coloring skills and refine hand movement, but cut pieces can also be glued in random patterns to colorful construction paper for an eye-catching art project. Store all extra pieces in a box or bag for use in other projects requiring paper scraps and trims.

Project Pages (pages 12–80)

Each project may be varied or changed to adapt to time constraints, ability level, and available supplies. You can modify projects to fit your students' skills by having some objects already cut out, or by using shape stamps or stickers. For cut-outs, instruct children to fold the area to be cut out in half and snip with their scissors. Then open out flat, insert scissors tip, and begin cutting to the shape of the cutout. Demonstrate this process, and then cut with them as they practice.

Put out different kinds of paper as your students' skills improve. Try a paper that is heavier, such as index card weight, or lighter, such as tracing or wrapping paper. Make a cutting center where the project of the week and all the materials children will need are readily available. Encourage children to use a hole punch and tweezers, as well as turkey basters, eye droppers, and squeeze bottles filled with paint to strengthen their scissors muscles and motor control.

Project Tips

If a pattern calls for puffy paint, you can mix equal parts of flour, salt, and water for a homemade version. Add food coloring or a bit of tempera paint for color.

Another "puffy paint" is royal icing, it takes color very well, but dries out fairly quickly. Although it is edible, instruct the children not to eat it.

Royal Icing Using Meringue Powder:

4 c (440 grams) confectioners' (powdered or icing) sugar

3 Tbsp. (30 grams) meringue powder

½–¾ cup (120–180 ml) warm water

Beat the confectioners' sugar and meringue powder with an electric or hand mixer until combined. Add water and beat on medium to high speed until stiff peaks form (5–7 minutes). To get the right consistency, add more powdered sugar or water, if necessary. You'll know you have the proper consistency when you lift the beater and the ribbon of icing that falls back into the bowl remains on the surface of the icing for a few seconds before disappearing. Makes about 3 cups.

Use or transfer the icing immediately to an airtight container to avoid hardening. Cover with plastic wrap when not in use.

Scissor Skills Assessment

Student Name	Skill	Correct Grasp	Straight Lines	Zigzags	Waves	Circles	Scallops	Spirals	Fringing	Steers paper, not scissors

Practice Page: Zigzags

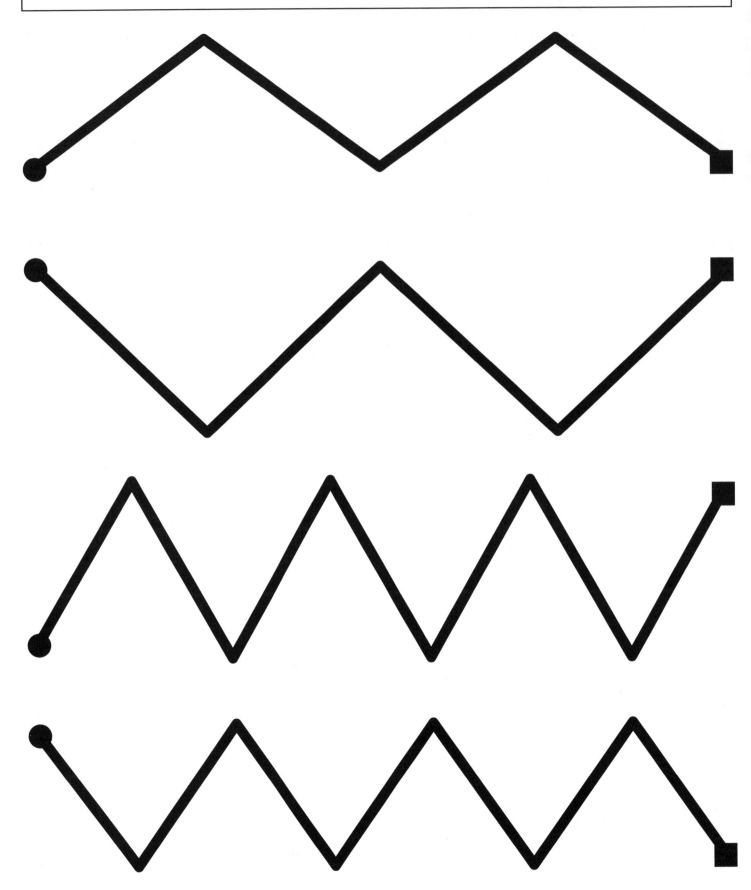

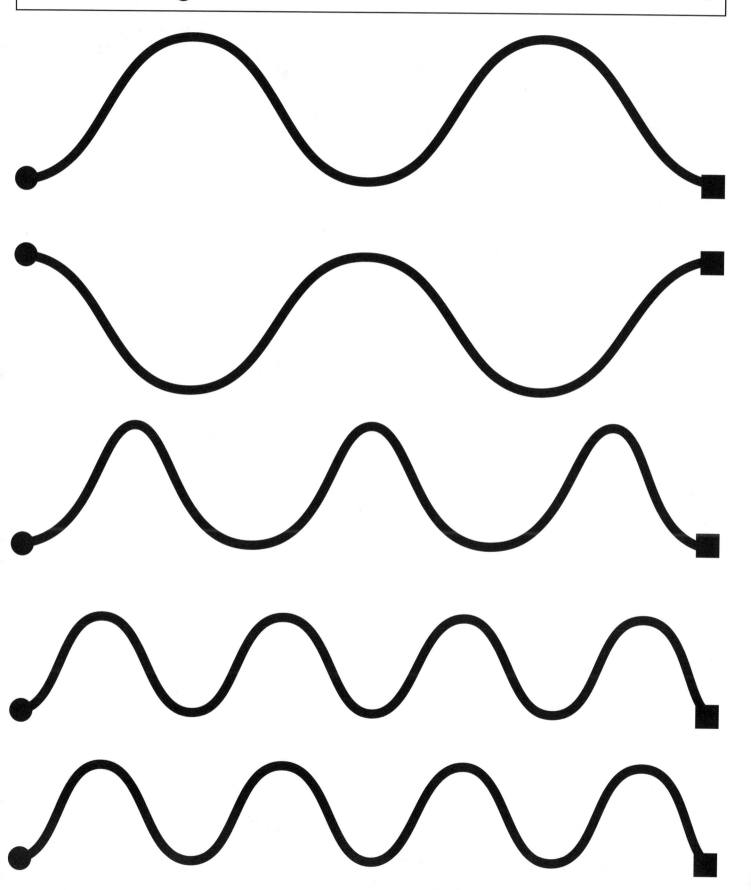

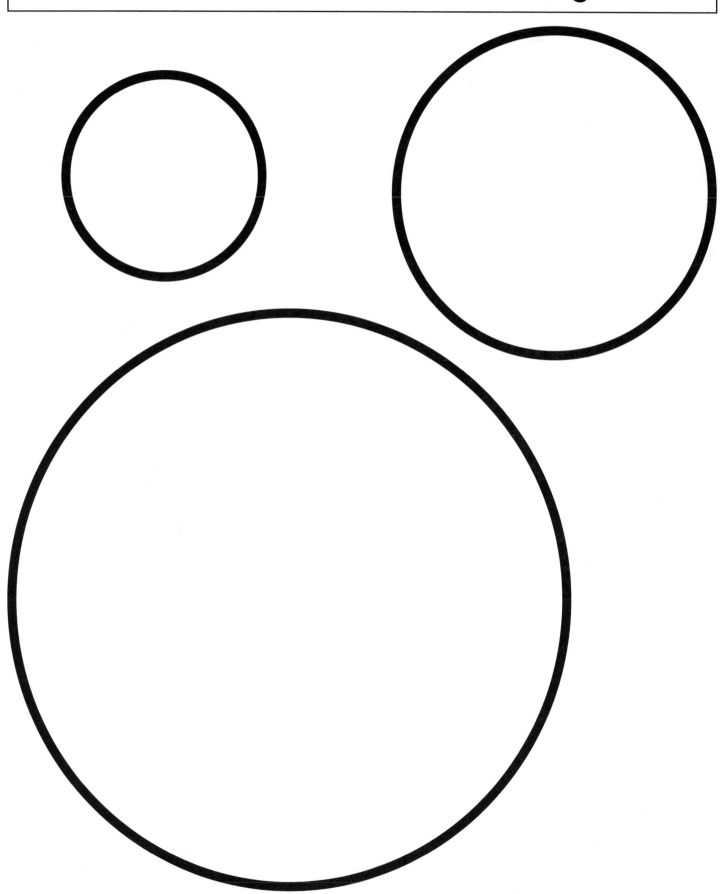

Practice Page: Scallops and Spirals

Practice Page: Fringing

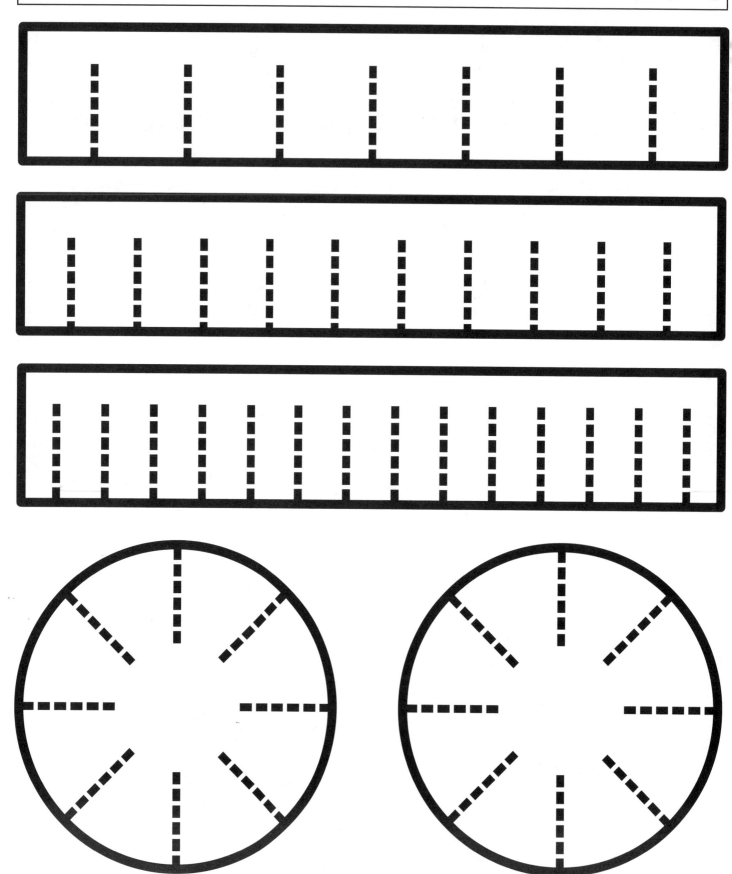

Apple

Skills
Curves, angles

Steps
Have children cut out shapes and color or paint them red or green. Have them draw a face on the worm and glue it to the apple. Alternatively, have children use a hole punch to make a hole in the apple and thread a green pipe cleaner through for a worm.

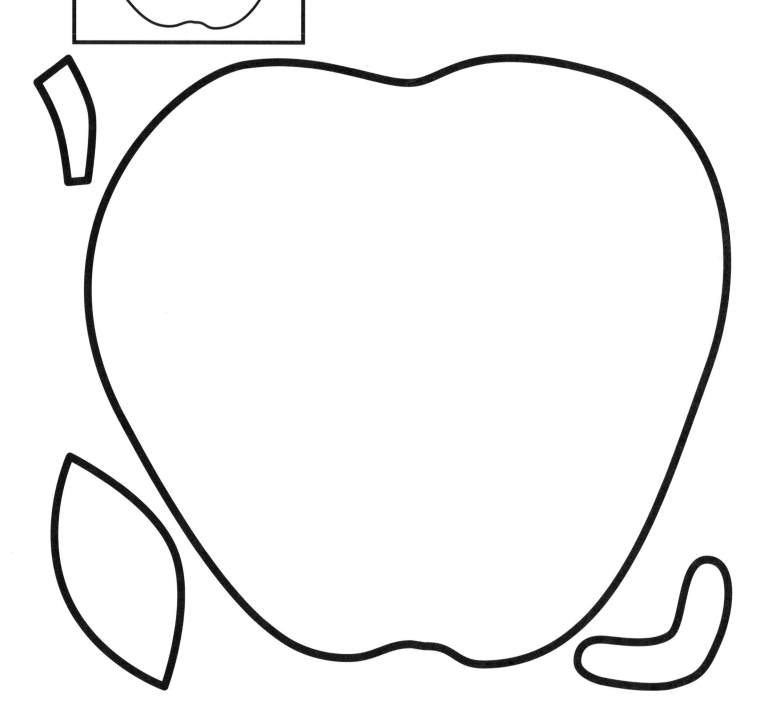

Football

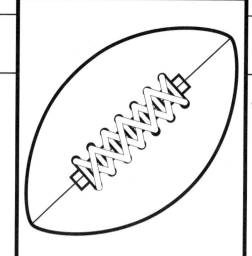

Skills

Large curves, lacing

Steps

Have children cut out and color the football. Show them how to fold the football in half along the seam, and have them use a hole punch to punch the holes at the end of the laces. Make sure they go through both layers of paper. Give the children white yarn to lace up the football.

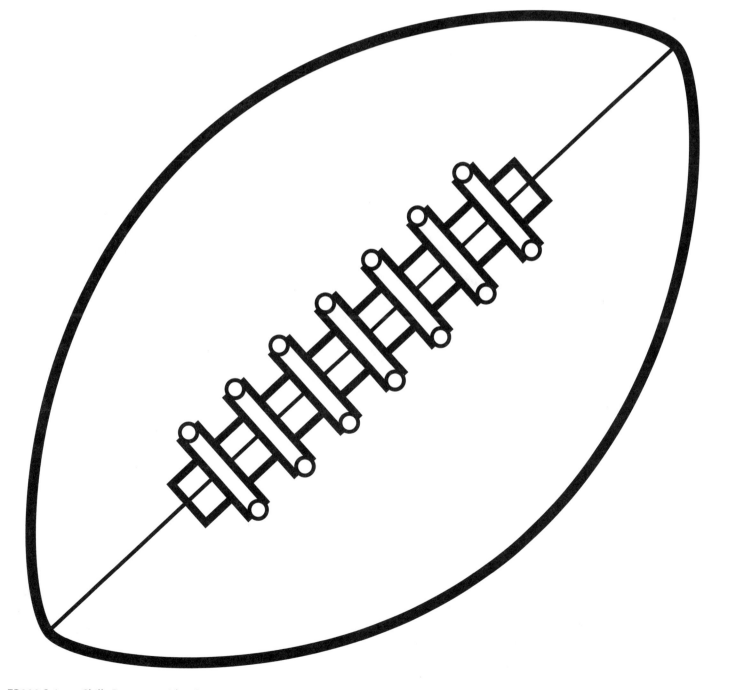

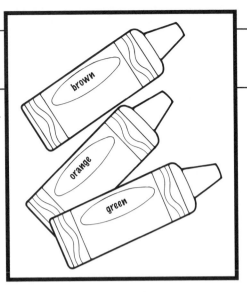

Crayon

Skills

Straight lines, angles

Steps

Reproduce and have children cut out several crayons. Help them write the names of different colors on the crayons. Then, have them color each crayon its correct color and use for recognition activities.

Family Picture Frame

Skills
Straight lines

Steps
Have children cut out the picture frame. Then, have them draw a scene of family members inside the frame. Alternatively, have children bring in a photograph to glue inside the frame.

EP009 Scissor Skills Patterns with a Purpose

Leaf

Skills

Large curves, scallops

Steps

Have children cut out the leaf. Let them tear orange, red, gold, and brown tissue into small pieces and glue them to the leaf to make fall colors.

Cheese

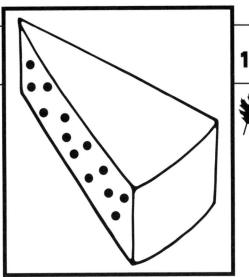

Skills

Straight lines

Steps

Have children cut out the cheese wedge and finger paint it orange. Talk about what different kinds of cheese look like. Let them use a hole punch to make Swiss cheese.

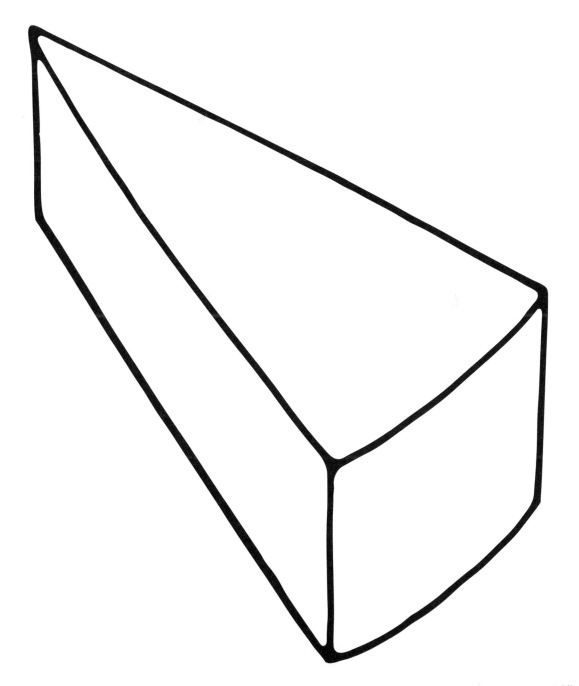

School Bus

Skills
Squares, straight lines, angles, circles

Steps
Have children cut out all the shapes. Show them how and where to glue windows, wheels, and the door onto the bus shape. Have them draw faces in the windows and detail with crayons.

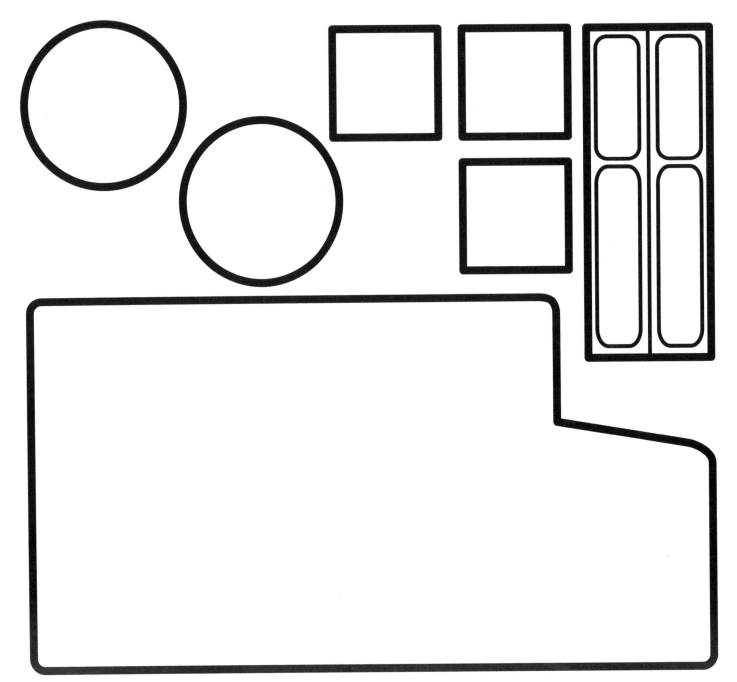

Ship

Skills

Scallops, straight lines, angles

Steps

Have children cut out the ship pieces and waves. Show them how to glue pieces to a sheet of blue construction paper to form a ship, using craft sticks for masts. Detail with watercolors or finger paint. Let them add clouds with puffy paint.

20

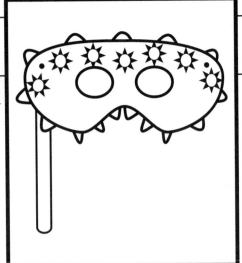

Mask

Skills
Large curves, cut-outs

Steps
Have children cut out masks, including eye holes, and decorate with stickers and fabric trims. Attach a band to fit the head, or tape onto a craft stick for an opera-style mask.

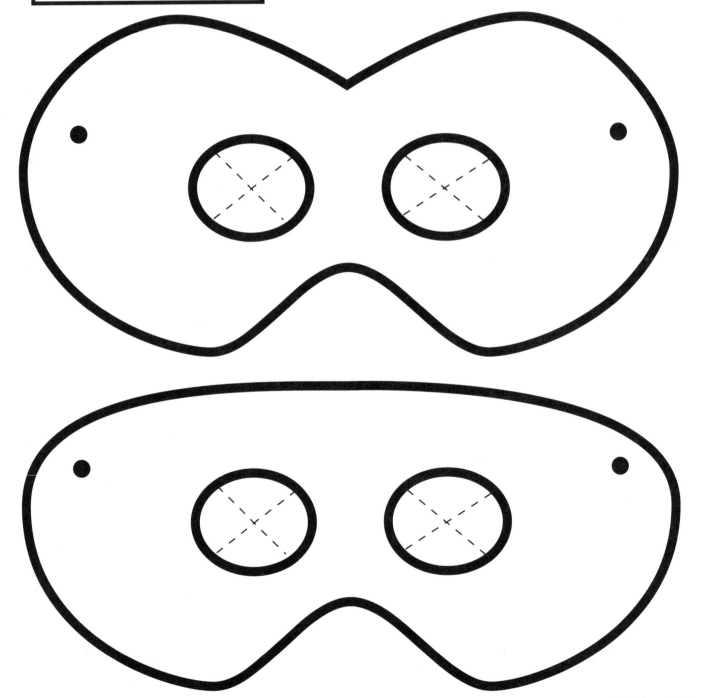

Jack-o'-lantern

Skills

Large curves

Steps

Have children cut out the pumpkin and color a face to turn the pumpkin into a jack-o'-lantern. Or, have the children draw a face on the pumpkin, and then instruct and demonstrate how to cut out the eyes, nose, and mouth. Let each child choose either a yellow or black piece of construction paper to place behind his or her pumpkin.

Black Cat

Skills
Curves, small angles

Steps
Have children cut out pieces and glue in the shape of a cat. Have them paint their cats black and glue on a yarn tail.

Ghost

Skills

Curved lines

Steps

Have children cut out the ghost as well as circles and ovals from black paper for eyes and mouth. For a challenge, have children cut the ghost out of heavy tracing paper.

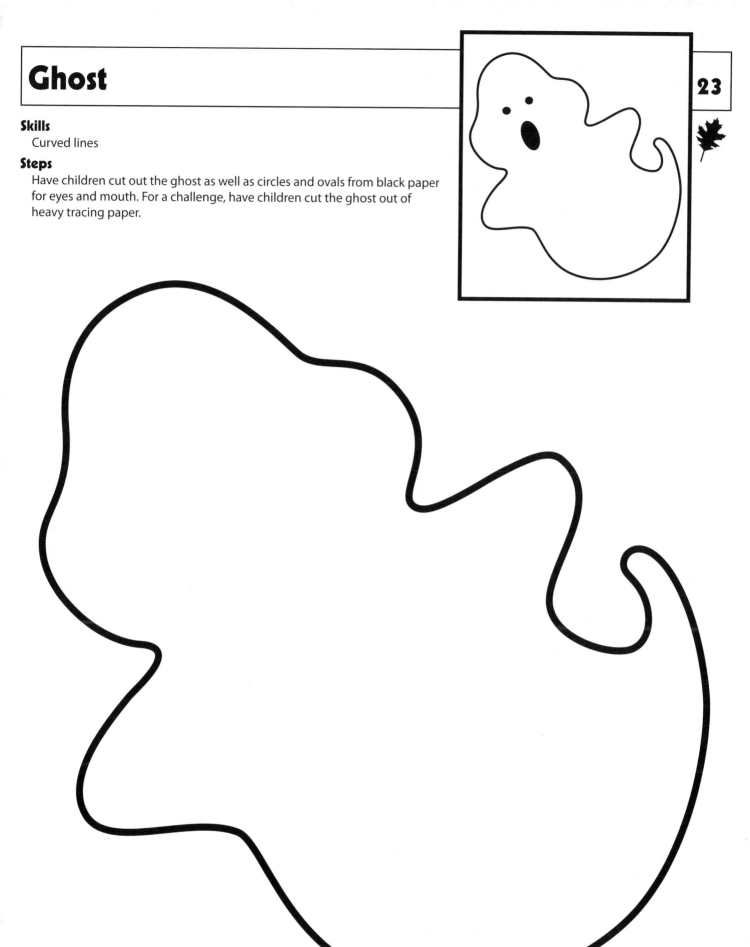

© Highsmith® Inc.

Witch

Skills
Angles, fringing

Steps
Have children cut out shapes and color a face and a black hat. Help them glue together as shown. Cut and curl fringed hair.

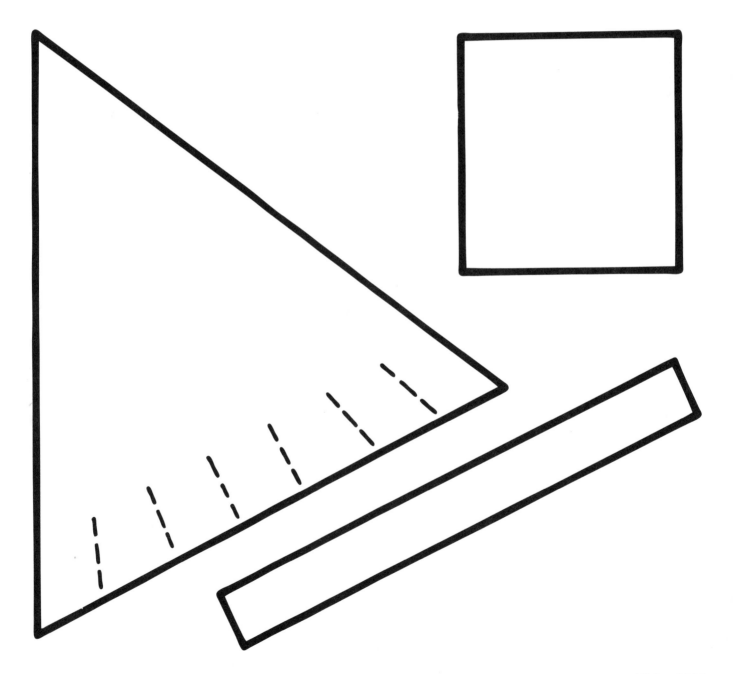

Pilgrim Hat

Skills
Solid, straight lines

Steps
Have children cut out and color the buckle yellow, and paste in place. Give each child a six-inch paper plate and have them draw a face on it. Paste under the hat.

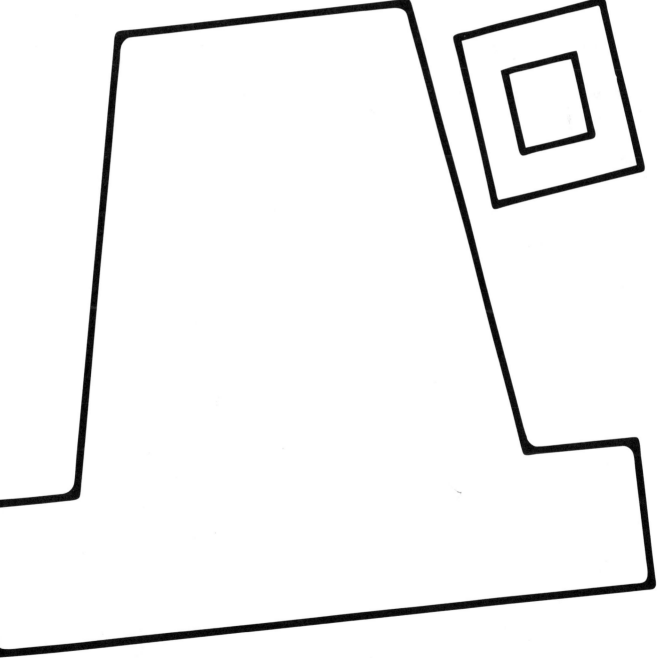

Turkey

Skills

Scalloped circles, small circle, small curves

Steps

Have children cut out the turkey parts, color them, and glue together as shown.

Corn

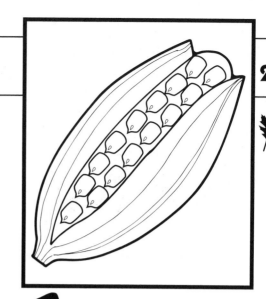

Skills

Large curves

Steps

Have children cut out and color the husk of the corn. Have them glue unpopped popcorn kernels to the ear of corn.

Blackbird Pie

Skills
Straight lines, large curve, scallops, small angles

Steps
Talk about the nursery rhyme, "Sing a Song of Sixpence." Have the children cut out the pie pieces, color, and glue to a sheet of paper. Leave enough space between the top and bottom crusts to fill the pie. Have the children cut out blackbirds to put in this pie. Or, let children fill their pie with drawings of their favorite pie filling.

Cornucopia

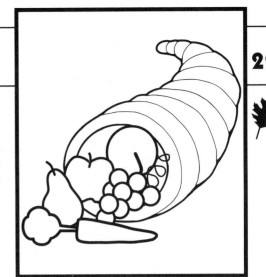

Skills
Large curves

Steps
Have the children cut out the cornucopia and color it. Provide old magazines and let them find and cut out pictures of fruits and vegetables to glue to the opening.

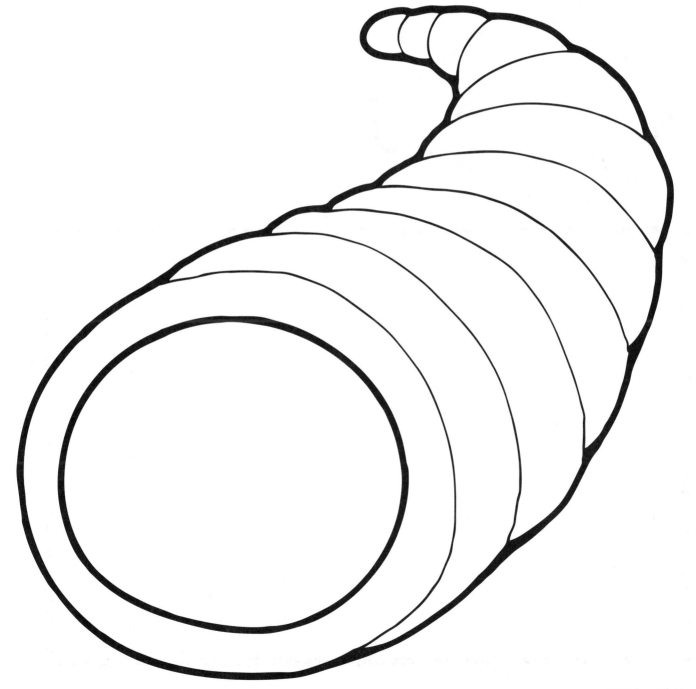

EP009 *Scissor Skills Patterns with a Purpose*

© Highsmith® Inc.

Candle

Skills
Straight lines, small curves

Steps
Have children cut out the candle and color it. Help them roll the candle to form a tube and glue to hold in place. Glue flame in place.

Santa

Skills
Straight lines, cut-out

Steps
Have children cut out the Santa, including the dotted line and the inside circle. Have them color a red hat and glue cotton balls to the beard. Hang on a doorknob.

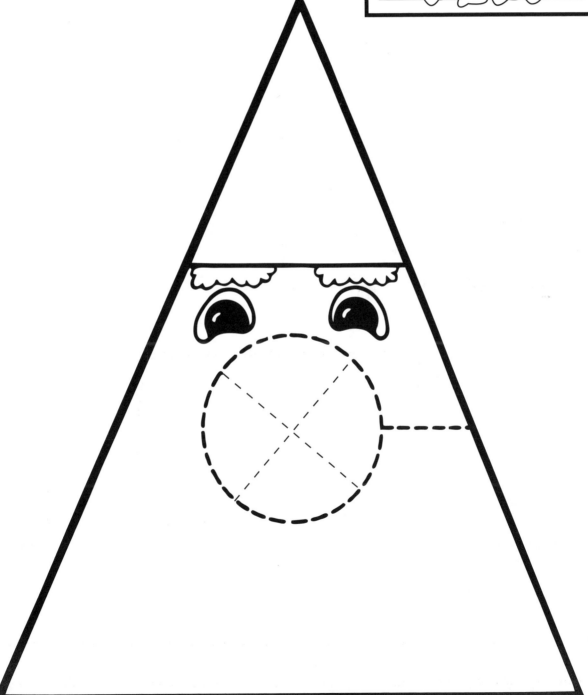

EP009 Scissor Skills Patterns with a Purpose

© Highsmith® Inc.

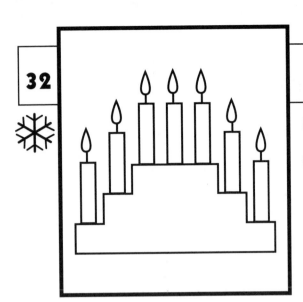

Kinara

Skills
Straight lines, angles

Steps
Have children cut out the kinara and separate candles. Color and glue to a sheet of paper. Children can make flames out of tissue, or they can use their fingerprints from a yellow stamp pad.

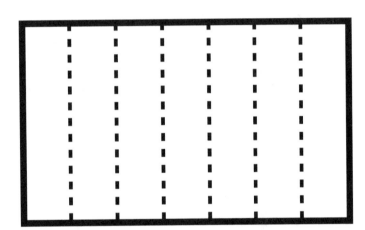

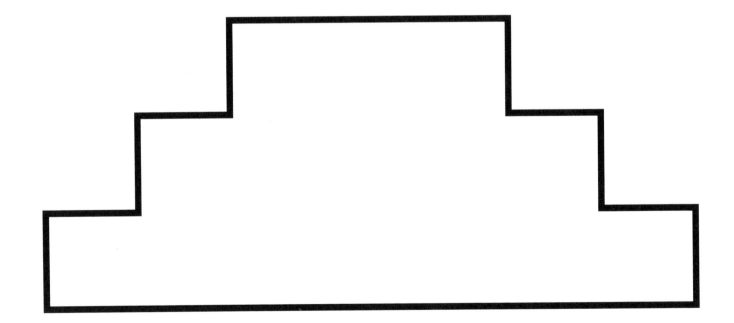

Holiday Tree

Skills
  Angles

Steps
  Have children cut out the tree and paint it green. Glue on fabric trim and candy pieces to decorate.

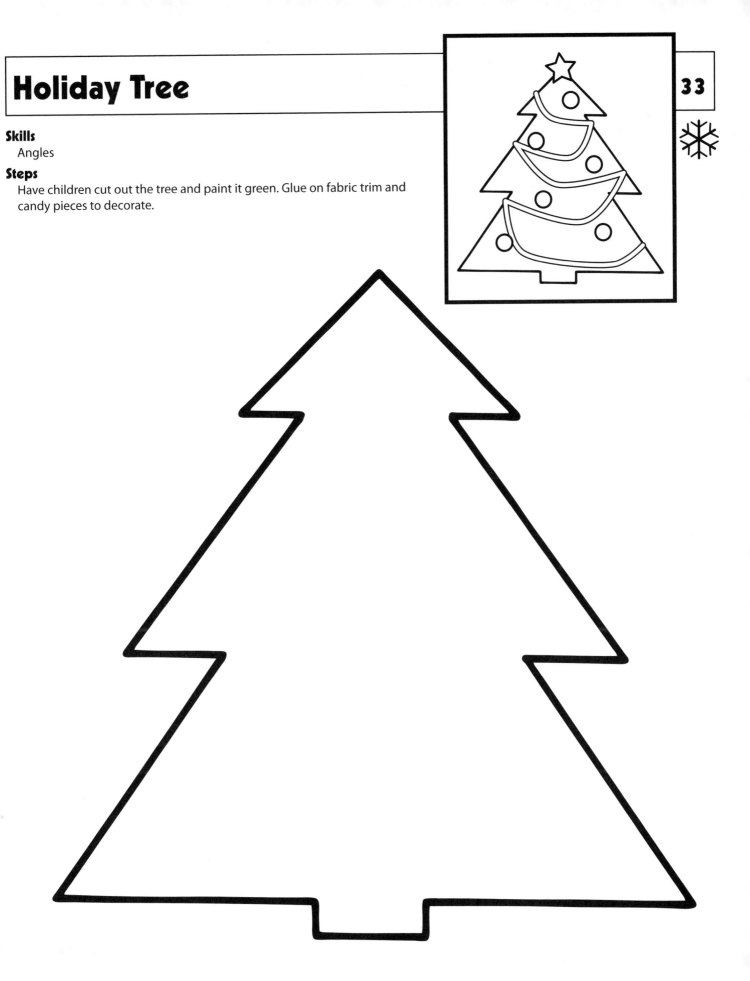

© Highsmith® Inc.

Reindeer

Skills
Curved lines, angles

Steps
Have children cut out reindeer and antlers. Let them paint or color and glue the reindeer to construction paper with the antler on top. Paste a red pom pon on the nose.

Present

Skills
Straight lines, small curves

Steps
Have children cut out the present and color the bow. Have them glue gift wrap on top of the present before adding the bow. Staple the bow and the top edge of the present box to a larger sheet of paper. Have children draw a present they would like to give or get on the paper under the wrapping. Adjust the size and shape of the box if needed.

I would give my dad three apples.

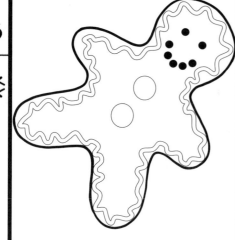

Gingerbread Man

Skills
Curves

Steps
Have children cut out the gingerbread man. Let them use puffy paint or royal icing for icing decorations. Use glue to add cake decorations and colored sugar. Share "The Gingerbread Man" story.

Penguin

Skills

Large curves, angles

Steps

Have children cut and color the penguin's body and wings black. Have them keep his tummy white. Help them assemble as shown. Color and fold the orange-colored beak in half before pasting.

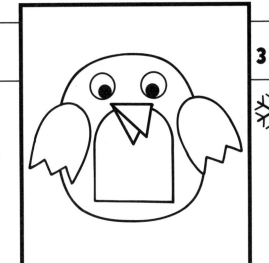

Polar Bear

Skills
Large and small curves

Steps
Have children cut out the polar bear and use puffy paint and a toothbrush to paint fur on the bear.

Dragon

Skills
Large and small curves, scallops, waves

Steps
Have children cut out and color the dragon. Have them staple colorful crepe paper streamers to the back of the dragon and glue a craft stick to the bottom back for a handle.

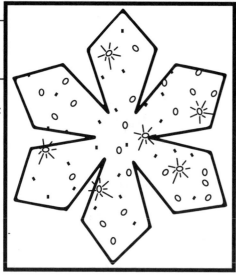

Snowflake

Skills
Small angles

Steps
Have children cut out their snowflakes. Provide hole punches of various shapes for children to add more detail to their snowflakes. Have them spread glue on the snowflake and sprinkle with sparkling glitter.

Snowman

Skills
Circles of various sizes, small curves

Steps
Have children cut out the three circles and mittens. Have them glue their snow person on construction paper and use toothpicks for arms and buttons for eyes, mouth, and buttons. Or, allow children to punch holes in black construction paper, using a hole punch. Use the resulting circles for the eyes, buttons, and mouth.

EP009 Scissor Skills Patterns with a Purpose

Lovebird

Skills
Curved lines, folding

Steps
Have children cut out hearts and color red. Remind children that these dotted lines are for folding, not cutting. Have children fold hearts in half, overlap, and glue. Have them illustrate the bird's eye and beak. You may wish to hole-punch the top of the bird's body to add string and hang from the ceiling.

Heart Letter

Skills

Large curves, folding

Steps

Cutting, coloring, folding

Suggestions

Have children cut out heart. Remind children that these dotted lines are for folding, not cutting. Have them fold the point of the heart up and then fold in the two "bumps." Have them dictate or write a message to someone they love in the middle. Encourage the children to deliver their letters.

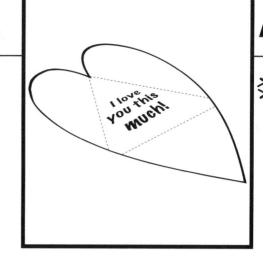

43

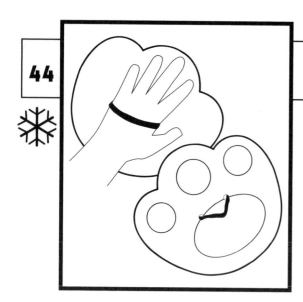

Paw Mitts

Skills
Large curves, scallops

Steps
Have children cut out paws and color them according to the animal they wish to be. Punch holes where indicated. Cut a 5– to 6-inch length of ¼-inch elastic. Thread the elastic through the hole and tie into a loop. Children can slip on their paws and pretend to be an animal!

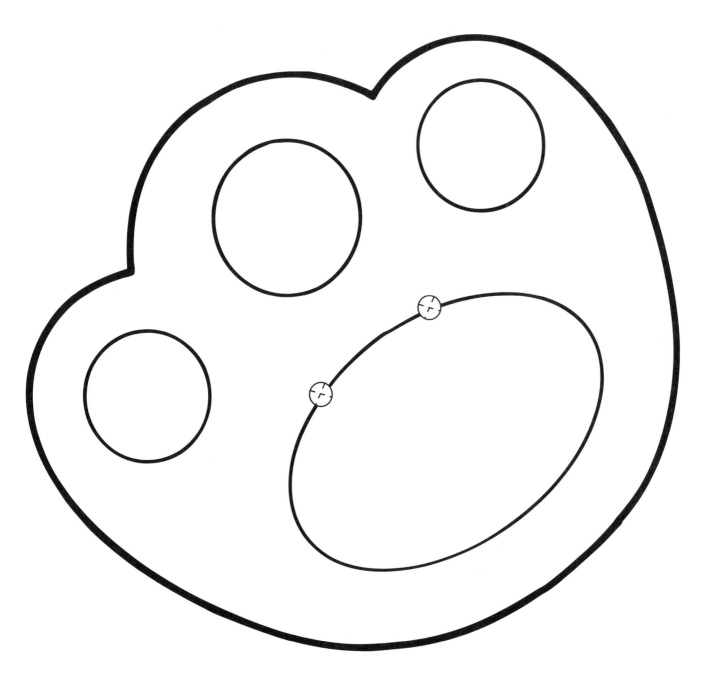

Weather Chart

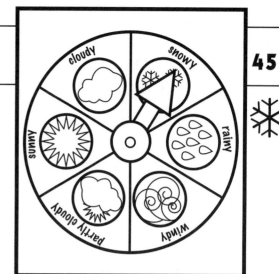

Skills

Circles, angles

Steps

Have children cut out the circles and the pointer. Have them glue the circles to the pie chart. Attach the pointer to the chart with a paper brad. Help children label their weather charts.

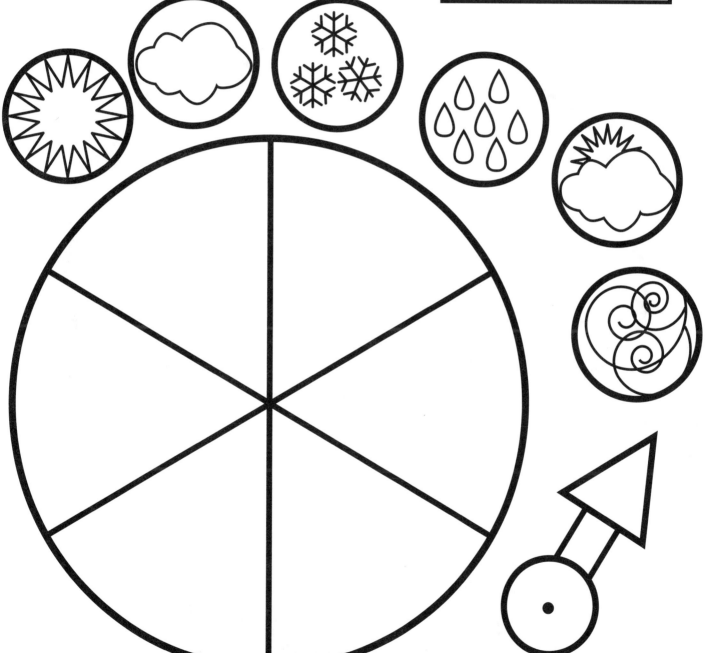

© Highsmith® Inc.

Cupcake

Skills

Straight lines, scallops

Steps

Have children cut out the cupcakes. They can "frost" the cupcake with puffy paint. Provide real birthday candles that they can glue on.

Peppermint

Skills

Large curves, small angles

Steps

Have children cut out candy. Let them snip off rectangles from a red strip of construction paper and glue to the peppermint around the edges. Or, let children finger paint their candies.

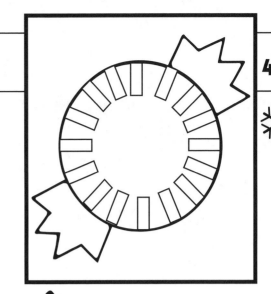

47

Woolly Lamb

Skills
Small circle, straight lines, curved lines

Steps
Have children cut out the lamb parts and color a landscape on construction paper. Help them paste cut-outs to form the lamb's body as shown. You may wish to let them glue cotton balls to the lamb's body for wool.

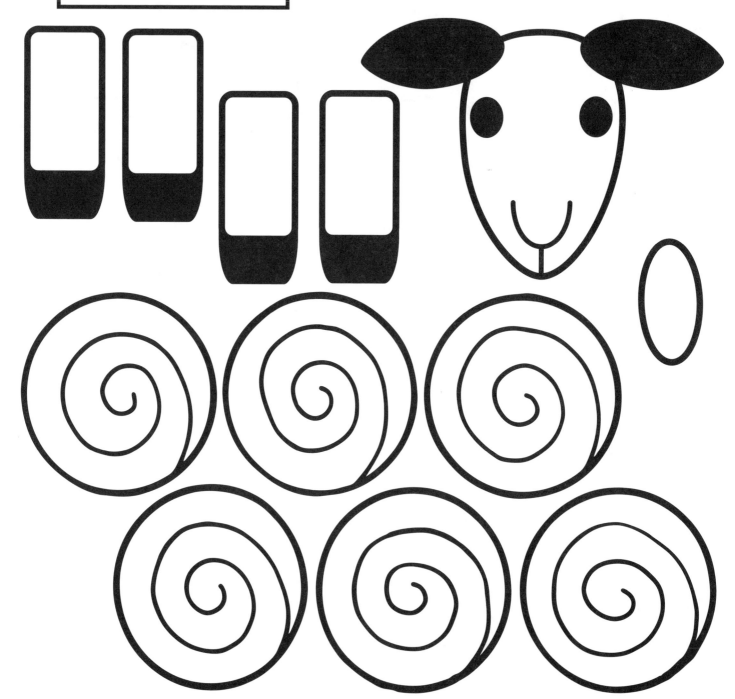

Leprechaun

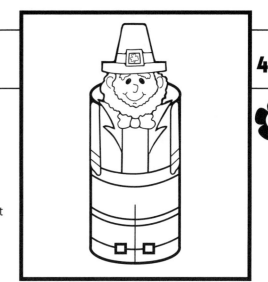

Skills

Solid lines, angles, curved lines

Steps

Have children cut and color the leprechaun. Have them roll the leprechaun around a toilet paper tube and tape or glue in the back. Variations: Stuff the ends of rainbow-colored tissue into the tube and allow to fan out to make a rainbow. Have children cut small "gold coins" from gold-colored paper to put into the tube.

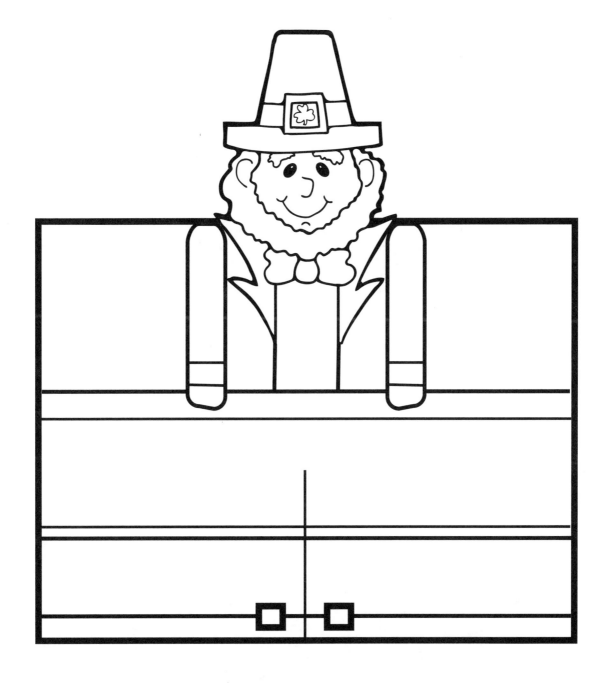

Lion

Skills
Large circles, fringe

Steps
Have children cut out the lion and color his face and mane. Have them cut on the dotted lines and curl the ends around a pencil to create a fluffy mane.

Shamrock

Skills

Curves

Steps

Have children cut out the shamrock. Have them dictate or write why they are lucky and write it on the shamrock. Have the children illustrate their statements.

Pig

Skills

Large curved lines, angles, small spiral

Steps

Have children cut out the pig. Have them cut the small circle into a spiral. Let them finger paint a brown background or spread real mud on construction paper. Allow to dry, then glue the tail and ear to the pig. Have them glue the pig in the mud.

Chick

Skills
Large circle, straight line, small scallops, curved lines, angles

Steps
Have children cut out chick pieces. Have them color the pieces and glue the wings, feet, and beak onto the chick.

© Highsmith® Inc.

Bunny

Skills
Large scallops

Steps
Have children cut out the bunny and color the front and back. Have them glue a fluffy cotton ball tail to the back of the bunny.

Hatching Egg

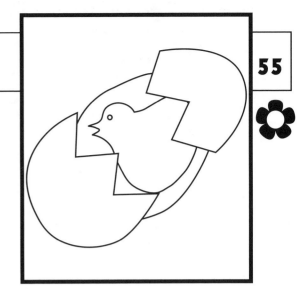

Skills
Large oval, zigzag lines

Steps
Have children cut out two egg shapes by taping two sheets of paper together when cutting out the large oval egg shape. Put the blank oval shape aside and have them cut on the zig-zag line on the first egg. Have children illustrate on the blank, whole egg what "hatched" out of their egg. Have them glue the broken egg on top of the whole egg.

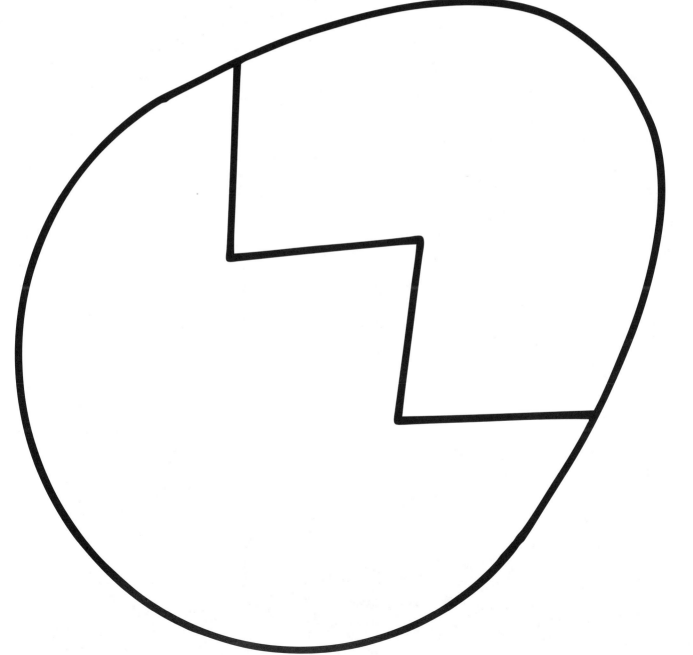

EP009 Scissor Skills Patterns with a Purpose

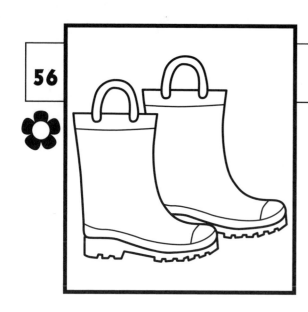

Muddy Boots

Skills
Large curves, small angles

Steps
Have children cut out and paint the boots. Let them use brown finger paint to make the boots muddy.

Umbrella

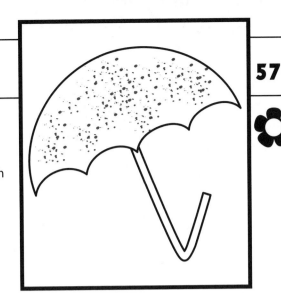

Skills
Large curves

Steps
Have the children cut out the umbrella. Let them use spray bottles filled with watercolor paint to spray color onto the umbrella. Tape a bendable plastic straw to the umbrella for a handle.

EP009 Scissor Skills Patterns with a Purpose

Carrot

Skills
Small scallops, curved lines

Steps
Have students cut out and color the top and bottom of the carrot. Have them glue coffee grounds "dirt" on the lower half of a piece of paper then glue the carrot root below and the carrot top above the ground.

Rain Cloud

Skills
Large scallops, small curves

Steps
Have students cut out the cloud and raindrops. Let them watercolor a rain cloud. Help them punch holes in the raindrops and the cloud and hang drops from the cloud with blue yarn.

EP009 Scissor Skills Patterns with a Purpose

© Highsmith® Inc.

Basket

Skills
Large curves, small ovals, cut-outs

Steps
Have children cut out the eggs and the basket, including the center. Let them color pretty eggs with water colors or finger paint to paste in the basket.

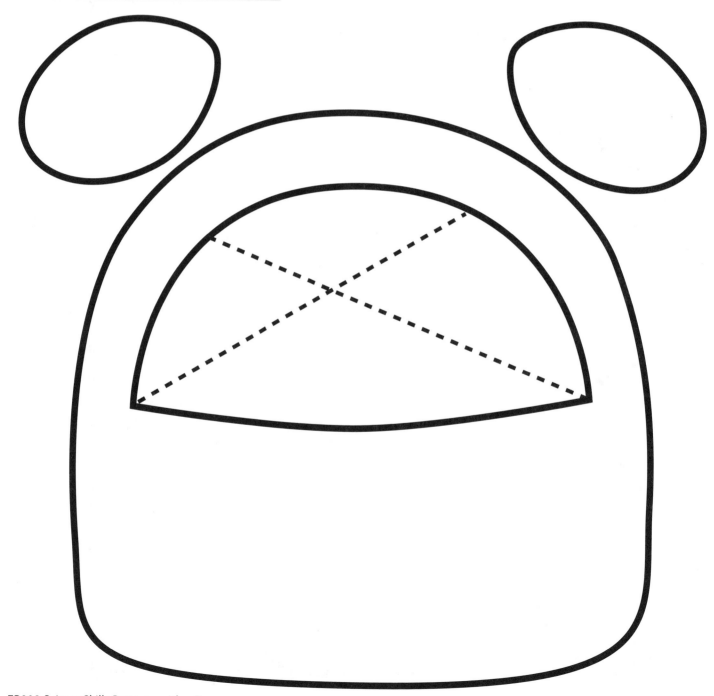

Spider

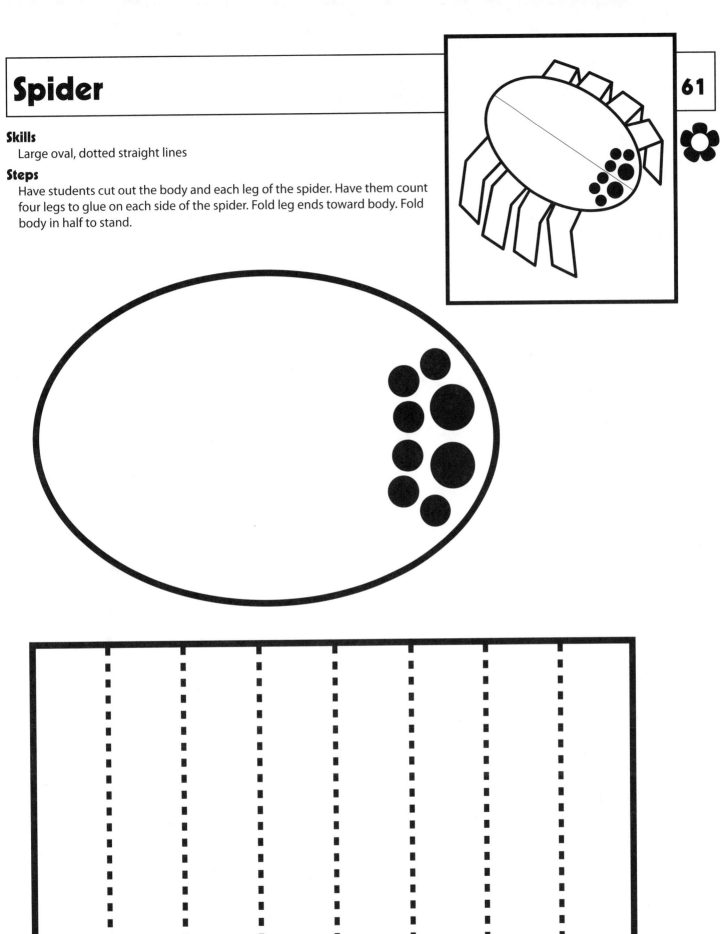

Skills
Large oval, dotted straight lines

Steps
Have students cut out the body and each leg of the spider. Have them count four legs to glue on each side of the spider. Fold leg ends toward body. Fold body in half to stand.

EP009 Scissor Skills Patterns with a Purpose

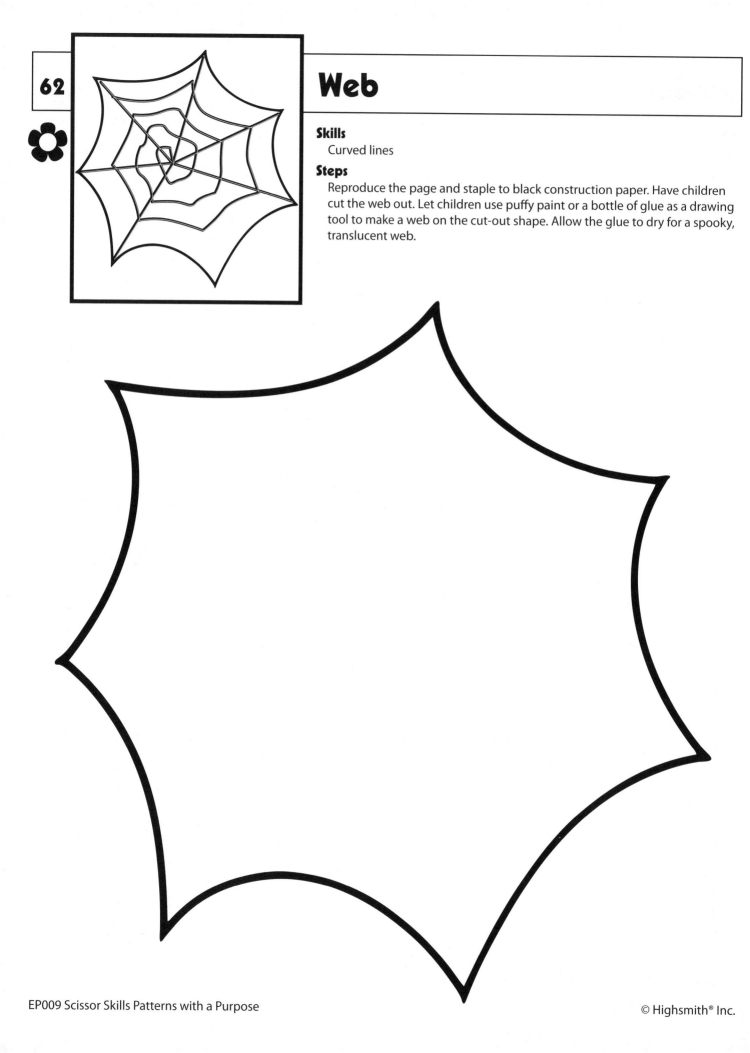

Web

Skills
Curved lines

Steps
Reproduce the page and staple to black construction paper. Have children cut the web out. Let children use puffy paint or a bottle of glue as a drawing tool to make a web on the cut-out shape. Allow the glue to dry for a spooky, translucent web.

Green Grass

Skills
Straight lines, fringing

Steps
Have children color and cut out bug and grass, fringing the edges. Have them color an outdoor scene on construction paper and "plant" grass. Have them glue colorful bugs in the grass.

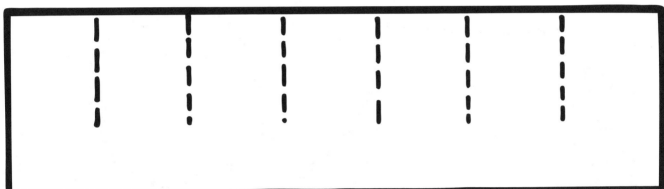

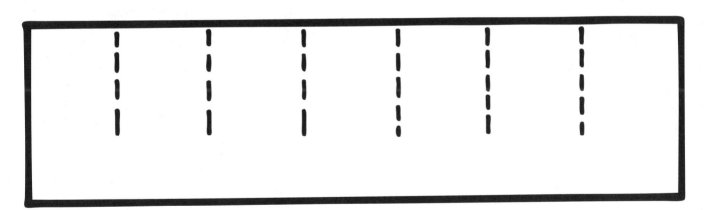

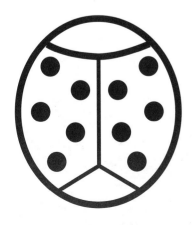

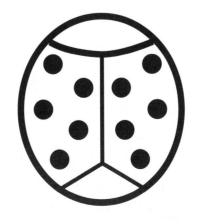

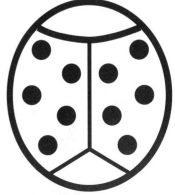

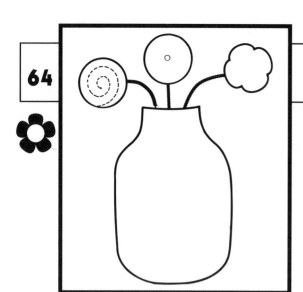

Flower-filled Vase

Skills
Large curve, small circle, scallops, spiral

Steps
Have children cut out vase and flowers, including the spiral flower. Help them create a flower arrangement. Add green pipe cleaners for stems.

Tulip

Skills
Large curve, straight lines, small angles

Steps
Have children cut out tulip pieces and write their names on the blooms. Have them color and glue the tulip and create a classroom "garden" on a large sheet of butcher paper.

Sun

Skills
Angles

Steps
Have children cut out the sun and its rays. Have them paint the sun yellow and, while still wet, sprinkle with orange or gold glitter.

Balloon

Skills

Large oval

Steps

Have the children cut out the balloon and paint it. Help them tie a piece of yarn to the end of the balloon.

© Highsmith® Inc.

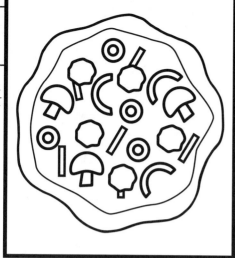

Pizza

Skills

Large waves, small circles, small waves, small curves

Steps

Reproduce the pizza and several sheets of ingredients for each child. Have children color, cut, and paste pizza ingredients onto the crust.

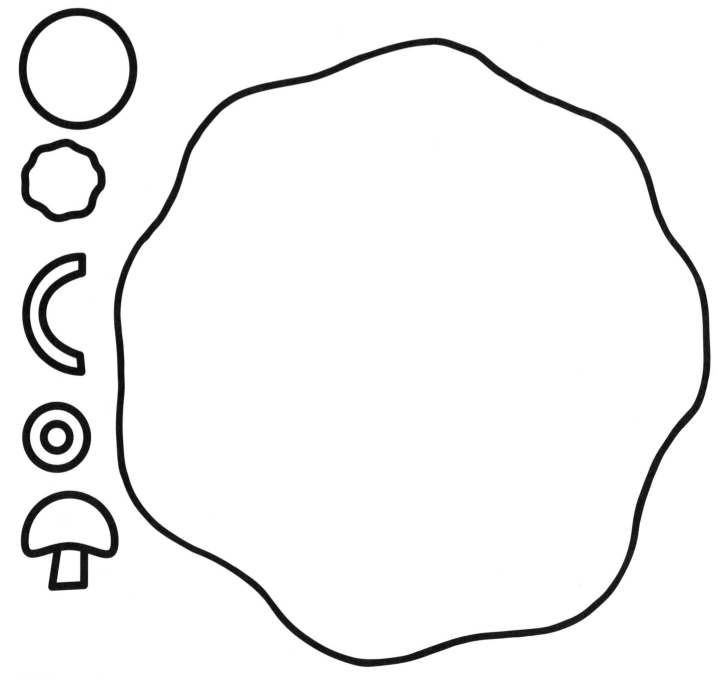

EP009 Scissor Skills Patterns with a Purpose

© Highsmith® Inc.

Blue Ribbon

Skills

Large circle, angles, fringe

Steps

Have students cut out the ribbon and write the number 1 on it. Have them fringe the top piece and glue the pieces together. Pin to a student's collar or shirt.

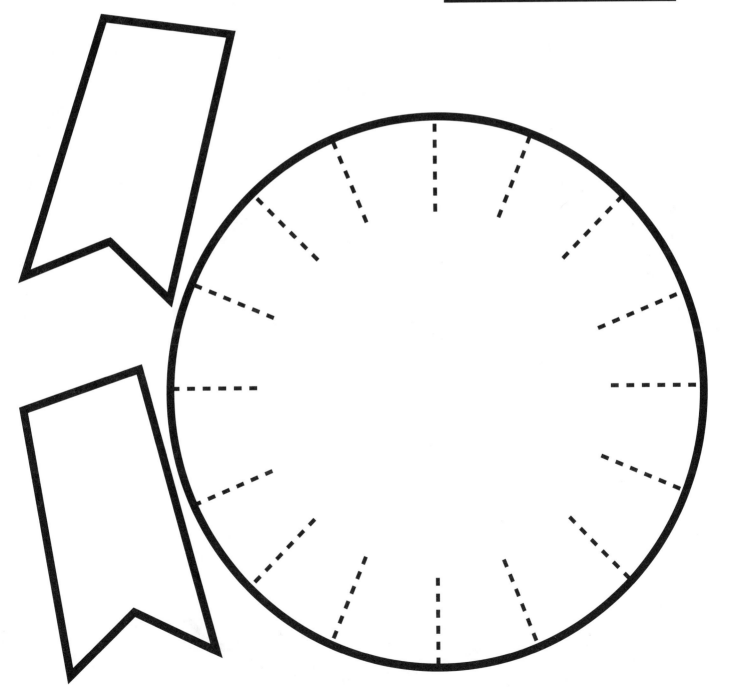

EP009 *Scissor Skills Patterns with a Purpose*

© Highsmith® Inc.

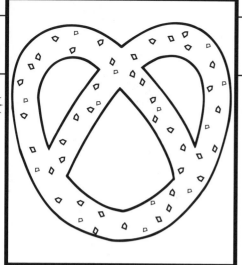

Pretzel

Skills
Large curves, cut-outs

Steps
Have children cut out the pretzel, including the inside cut-outs. Have children use fingertips to spread glue on the colored pretzel and sprinkle with kosher salt.

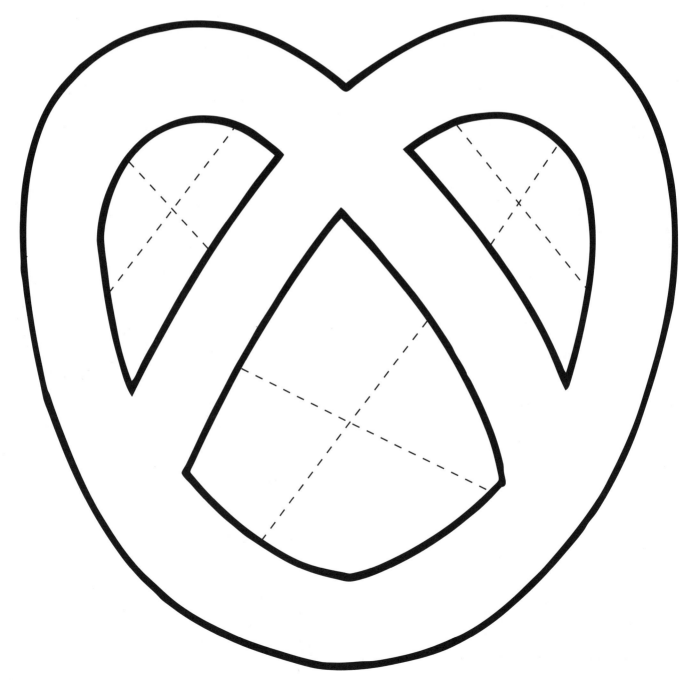

Root Beer Float

Skills

Straight lines, scallops, cut-outs

Steps

Have children cut out the root beer float, including the inside of the handle. Let them use shaving cream or puffy paint to paint the foamy top. Glue a real straw in the root beer float.

Turtle

Skills

Curves, scallops, straight line

Steps

Have children cut out turtle and tail. Have them cut the dotted line and help them overlap the sides of the shell and glue to create a 3-D look. Let children cut up green and brown construction paper into various polygons. After cutting and assembling the turtle, children can glue construction paper shapes onto the turtle shell.

Sailboat

Skills

Straight lines, angles

Steps

Have children cut out the ship and color. Have them paste it to a sheet of blue construction paper, using a craft stick for the mast. Let them use glue to "paint" foamy waves and add cotton balls for clouds.

J67

EP009 Scissor Skills Patterns with a Purpose

Lollipop

Skills
Large circle

Steps
Have the children cut out the lollipop and finger paint colorful swirls. Have them glue the lollipop to a craft stick.

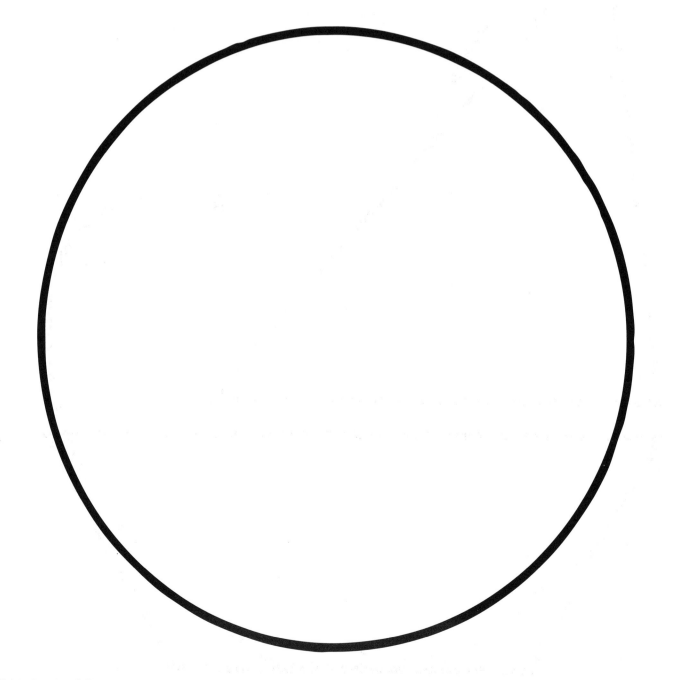

Cactus

Skills

Curved lines

Steps

Have children cut out the cactus and sponge paint it. Cut toothpicks in half and have children glue toothpicks to the cactus to resemble spines.

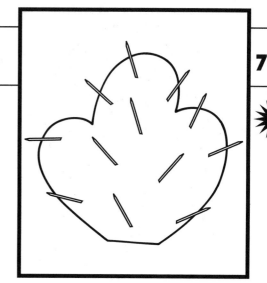

75

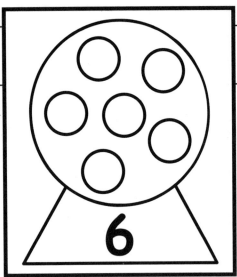

Gum Balls

Skills
Large circle, small circles, straight lines

Steps
Have children cut out the gum balls and the machine and color gum balls in assorted colors. Have the children glue the gum balls in the machine and identify the colors. Have them count the gum balls and write the number on the base.

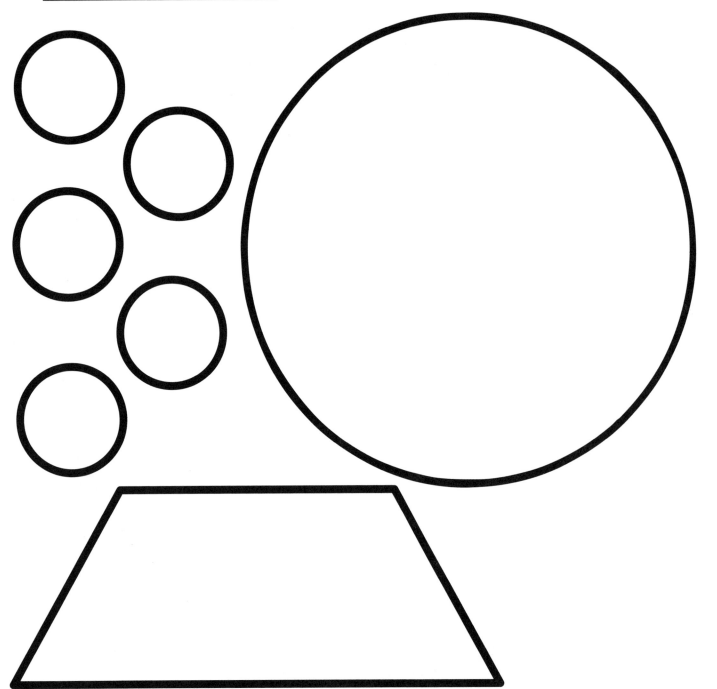

Stars and Stripes Collage

Skills
Dotted straight lines, angles

Steps
Have the children cut out the stars and the individual stripes. Have them color patriotic stars and stripes and glue to contrasting paper.

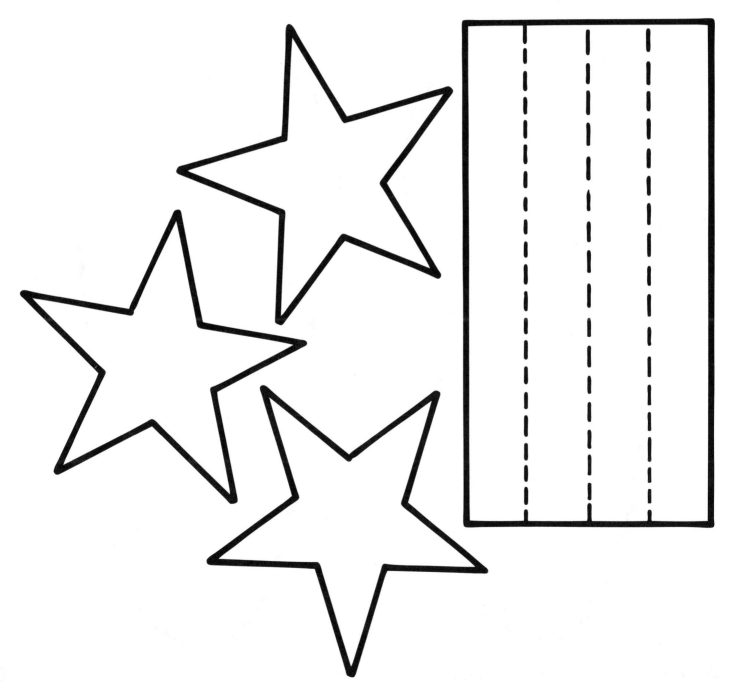

© Highsmith® Inc.

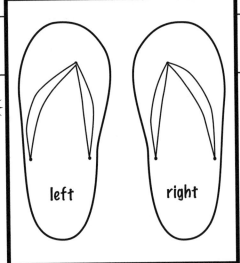

left   right

Flip-flops

Skills

Large curves

Steps

After children cut out flip-flops, have them hole punch where indicated and use yarn, ribbon, or paper to add the thongs. Help children label their flip-flops "right" and "left."

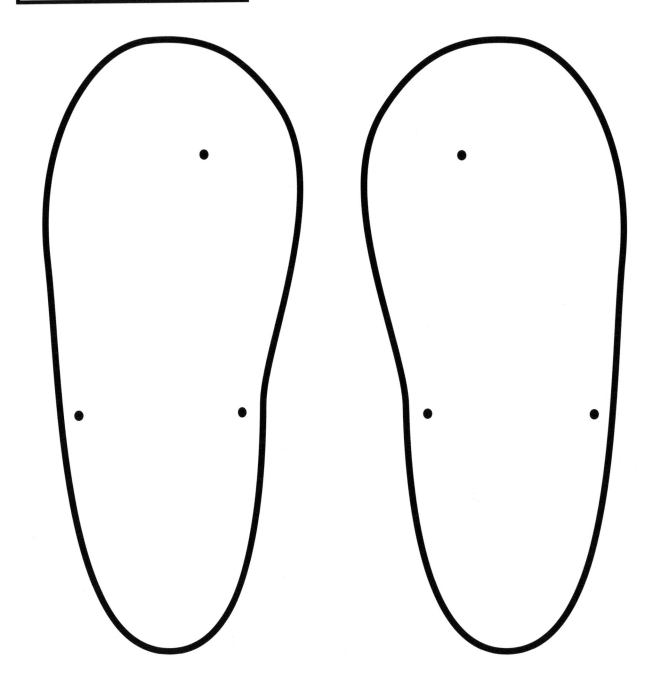

Tent

Skills
Straight lines

Steps
Have children cut out the tent shape, making sure to cut the dotted line for the flap opening. Have them glue the tent to another sheet of paper, making sure not to glue the flap down. Instruct children to draw a picture of who is camping out in the tent and add stars, moon, and other wilderness to the scene.

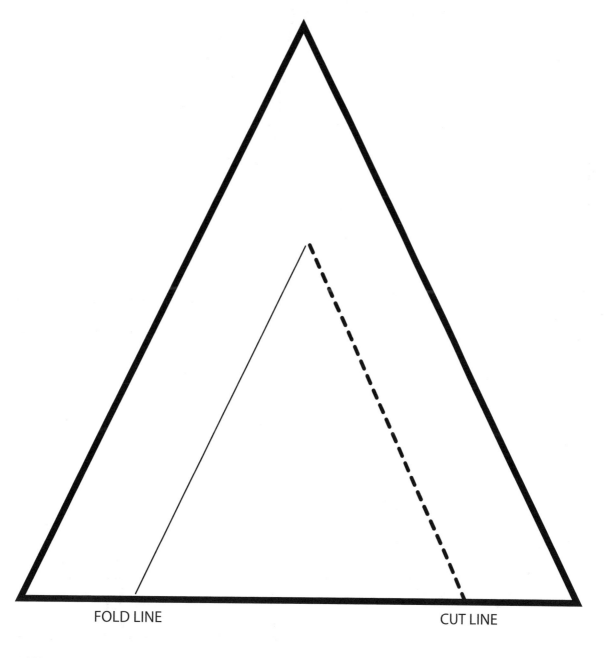

FOLD LINE   CUT LINE

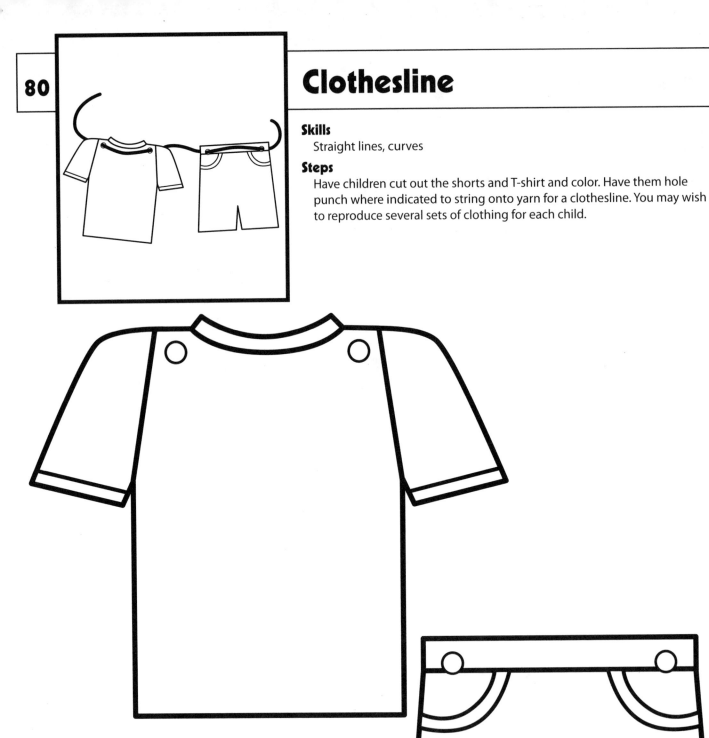

Clothesline

Skills

Straight lines, curves

Steps

Have children cut out the shorts and T-shirt and color. Have them hole punch where indicated to string onto yarn for a clothesline. You may wish to reproduce several sets of clothing for each child.